HEY!

HEY, *ALEX!* HOLD ON!

ARE YOU *DOING* ANYTHING TONIGHT?

YEAH. *DOUBLE FRENCH AND HISTORY.* SORRY, SABINA.

ALEX, ARE YOU *OK*? I'VE HARDLY *SEEN* YOU ALL WEEK, AND YOU SEEM—

I'M *FINE*.

I'M *SORRY*.

IT'S NOT BEING ABLE TO *TELL* ANYONE, YOU KNOW? HAVING ALL MY *FRIENDS* THINK I WAS OFF FOR TWO WEEKS WITH *FLU*, THAT I'M SOME *PAMPERED IDIOT*...

IT'S DRIVING ME *MAD*.

BORED, MORE LIKE.

YOU CAN'T WAIT FOR YOUR *SECRET AGENT BEEPER* TO GO OFF AGAIN, THAT'S YOUR TROUBLE.

I TOLD YOU, I'M *NOT* A SPY.

IT *WOULD* BE MORE EXCITING THAN *DOUBLE HOMEWORK*, THOUGH.

ANYWAY...

IT'S NOT *JUST* YOU WHO ISN'T ALLOWED TO TALK ABOUT IT, REMEMBER?

I HAD TO SIGN...

SABINA? WHAT IS IT?

THAT MAN IN THE *SKODA'S* HERE AGAIN.

THE *DRUG DEALER*.

YOU KNOW LUCY STILES WAS *BEATEN UP* THE OTHER DAY FOR HER *LUNCH MONEY*?

AND IT WENT STRAIGHT TO *SKODA*. SOMEBODY SHOULD *DO* SOMETHING ABOUT HIM.

YEAH.

THINGS HAVE BEEN *STOLEN*, TOO. HE'S *POISONING* THIS SCHOOL.

ANYWAY, I HAVE TO GO. I'LL SEE YOU *TOMORROW*, OK?

SURE. TAKE CARE!

HMMM...

WHAT'S HE *DOING* IN THERE?

HERE GOES NOTHING...

EW.

IT'S A FLOATING **DRUGS** FACTORY...!

SOMEBODY SHOULD **DO** SOMETHING ABOUT HIM.

MAYBE I SHOULD CALL THE **POLICE**.

...

OR BETTER **YET**...

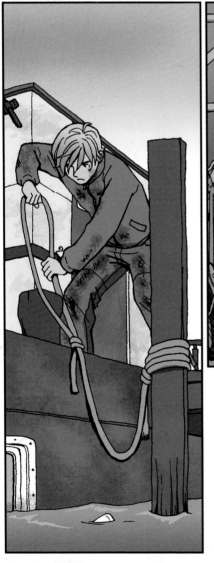

WOW.

WELL, *THIS* LOOKS EASY ENOUGH.

START

BEEP

WHIR RR

SO I *SAID* TO 'IM, IF THAT'S *STRAIGHT* I'M A *DUTCHMAN*...

TOO RIGHT.

ZMMMMMM

STEADY, STEADY...

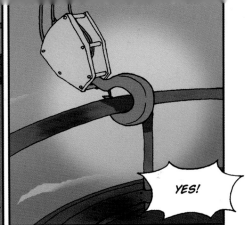

YES!

HOW'D IT GO TODAY?

SOLD A *HUNDRED QUID'S* WORTH. *MUGS,* THE LOT OF 'EM.

BRILLIANT. WE'LL HAVE THE *WHOLE SCHOOL—*

R...RRRRROINK!

AAH!

WE'RE *SINKING!*

WHAT WAS *THAT?*

CRANE OPERATOR, THIS IS BASE! WHAT THE HELL DO YOU THINK YOU'RE DOING? OVER!

WHO IS THAT UP THERE? IDENTIFY YOURSELF!

HURRY UP, ALEX...

OPERATOR, LOWER THE HOOK! WE BELIEVE THERE ARE PEOPLE INSIDE THAT BOAT! YOU ARE ENDANGERING THEIR LIVES!

I REPEAT, LOWER THE HOOK!

YEAH, YEAH. JUST LET ME GET THEM TO THE *POLICE STATION*, I'M NOT GOING...

...ANYWHERE.

RRRRR...

ULP.

KOF! KOF!

WHAT THE...?

ERM...

HELLO.

DO YOU...

DO YOU HAVE *ANY* IDEA WHAT YOU'VE JUST *DONE?*

I WAS JUST WORKING ON THE *CRIME FIGURES.*

I THINK THERE'S BEEN A *DROP.*

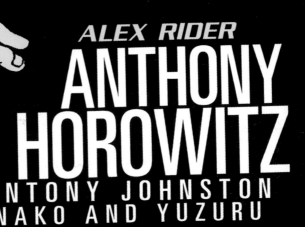

ALEX RIDER

ANTHONY HOROWITZ

ANTONY JOHNSTON
KANAKO AND YUZURU

THE GRAPHIC NOVEL

WALKER

POINT BLANC

First published 2007 by Walker Books Ltd
87 Vauxhall Walk, London SE1 1 5HJ

This edition published 2012

2 4 6 8 10 9 7 5 3 1

Text and illustrations © 2007 Walker Books Ltd
Based on the original novel *Point Blanc* © 2001 Stormbreaker Productions Ltd

Trademarks © 2009 Stormbreaker Productions Ltd
Alex Rider™, Boy with Torch Logo™, AR Logo™

This book has been typeset in Wild Words and Serpentine Bold

Printed in China

British Library Cataloguing in Publication Data:
a catalogue record for this book is available from the British Library

ISBN 978-1-4063-4092-1

www.walker.co.uk

GOOD MORNING, ALEX.

MR CRAWFORD...

I **WONDERED** WHY NOBODY WOULD **TALK** TO ME AFTER THEY RAN MY NAME THROUGH THE **COMPUTER**.

YOU CAN COME WITH ME, NOW. WE'RE **LEAVING**.

WHERE **IS** EVERYONE? WHERE DID ALL THE **POLICEMEN** GO?

DON'T ASK **SILLY QUESTIONS**, ALEX. THIS WAY, PLEASE.

WHAT ABOUT MY **BIKE?** I LEFT IT BY THE BRIDGE...

DON'T WORRY, WE'VE **GOT** IT. AND YOUR **SCHOOLBOOKS**.

I HADN'T EXPECTED TO SEE YOU AGAIN SO **SOON**.

THAT'S JUST WHAT **I** WAS GOING TO SAY.

WHAT ON EARTH WERE YOU **THINKING?** YOU'VE DONE AN **ENORMOUS** AMOUNT OF DAMAGE. YOU PRACTICALLY **DESTROYED** A **TWO MILLION POUND** CONFERENCE CENTRE.

IT'S A MIRACLE NO ONE WAS **KILLED!**

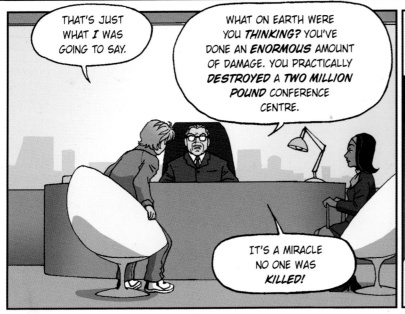

THE MEN IN THE BOAT WILL BE IN **HOSPITAL** FOR **MONTHS**.

AND YOU COULD HAVE KILLED THE **HOME SECRETARY**, ALEX.

THEY'RE **DRUG DEALERS**.

SO WE'VE DISCOVERED. BUT THE **NORMAL** PROCEDURE IS TO CALL **999**.

I COULDN'T FIND A PHONE.

SIGH

WE WERE THINKING OF **CONTACTING** YOU, ANYWAY. WE **NEED** YOU AGAIN.

THIS IS **MICHAEL J. ROSCOE**, HEAD OF **ROSCOE ELECTRONICS**, ONE OF THE LARGEST COMPANIES IN **AMERICA**.

COMPUTERS, VIDEOS, DVD PLAYERS, MOBILE PHONES, WASHING MACHINES... ROSCOE WAS **VERY** RICH, **VERY** INFLUENTIAL—

AND **VERY** SHORT-SIGHTED, ACCORDING TO THE **NEWS**.

HE FELL DOWN A **LIFT SHAFT** A FEW WEEKS AGO, DIDN'T HE?

IT CERTAINLY **SEEMS** TO HAVE BEEN A CARELESS ACCIDENT. THE LIFT **MALFUNCTIONED**, ROSCOE DIDN'T **LOOK** WHERE HE WAS GOING, HE FELL INTO THE SHAFT AND **DIED**.

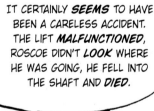

BUT WE'RE NOT SO **SURE**.

ON THE DAY ROSCOE DIED, AN **ENGINEER** CALLED AT **ROSCOE TOWER** TO CHECK A **DEFECTIVE CABLE**.

BUT THE COMPANY THAT **EMPLOYED** HIM SAY THERE **WAS** NO DEFECTIVE CABLE AND THEY NEVER **SENT** HIM TO THE TOWER.

SO WHY DON'T YOU ASK **HIM?**

OH, WE'D **LIKE** TO. BUT HE'S **VANISHED** WITHOUT TRACE. IT'S POSSIBLE HE WAS **KILLED**, AND SOMEONE ELSE TOOK HIS **PLACE** TO SET UP ROSCOE'S "ACCIDENT".

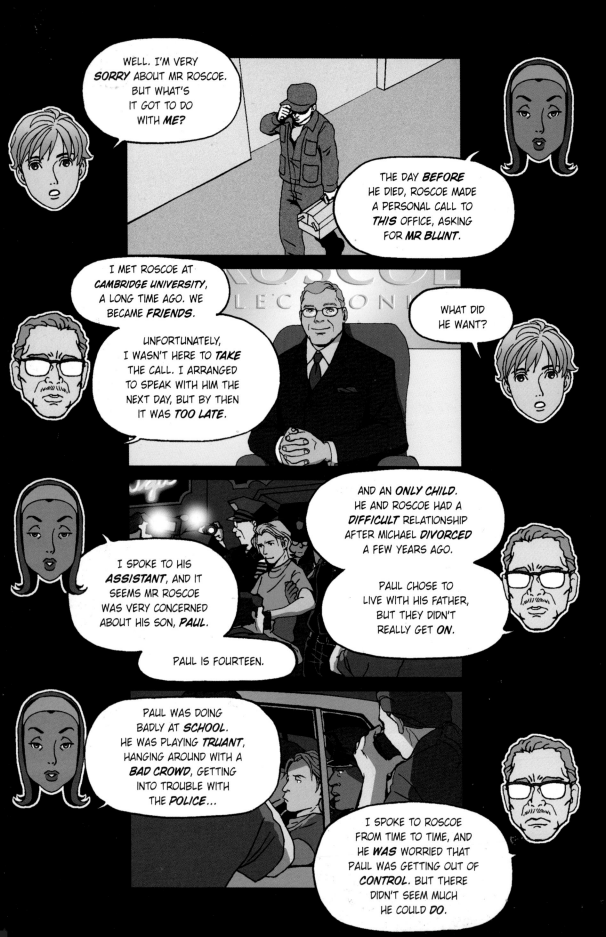

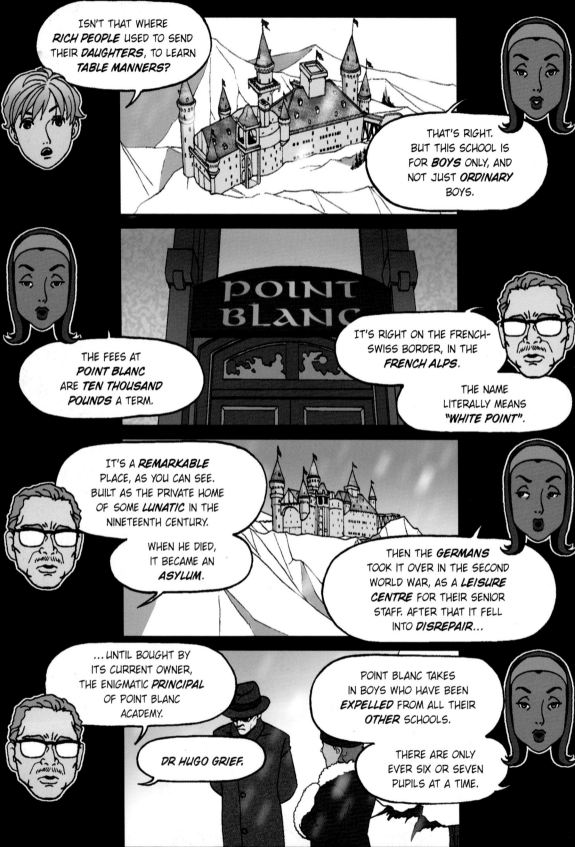

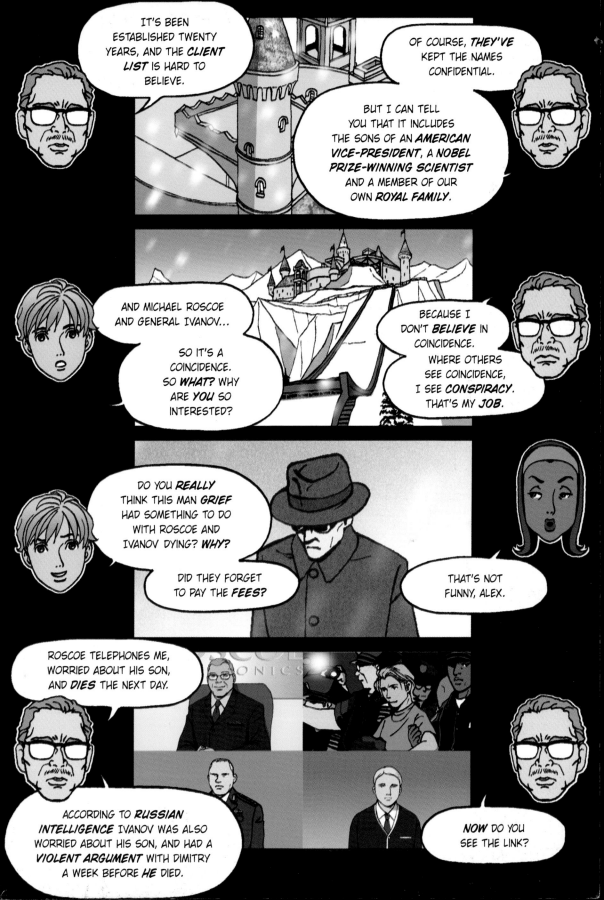

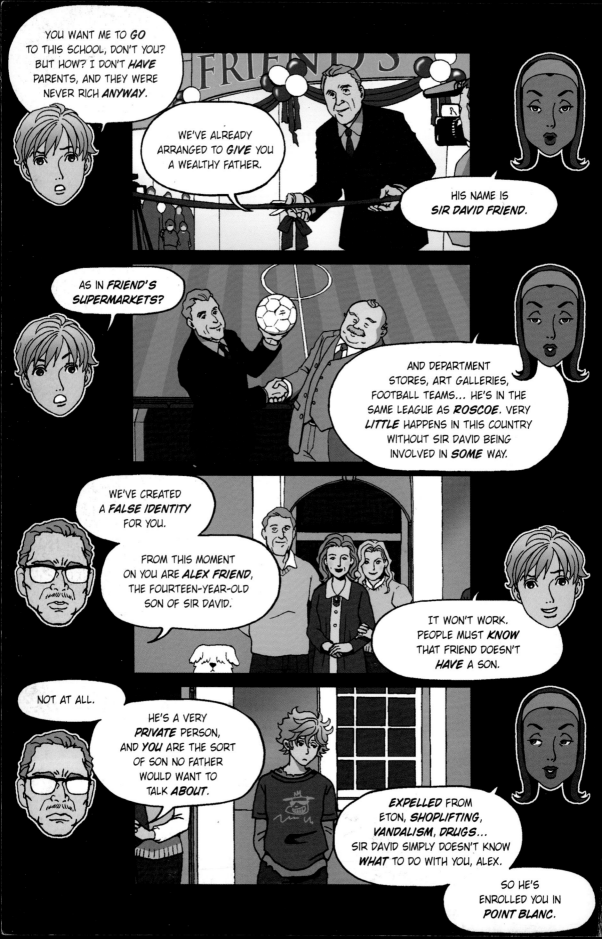

I HAVE DECIDED TO MOVE THE *GEMINI PROJECT* INTO ITS *LAST PHASE*.

POINT BLANC ACADEMY, FRANCE

I UNDERSTAND, DOCTOR.

BUT ARE YOU SURE WE'RE *READY?*

WITH *TWO* UNSATISFACTORY RESULTS IN THE LAST FEW MONTHS, WE HAVE *NO* CHOICE.

BESIDES THE EXPENSE OF *ARRANGING* THOSE TERMINATIONS, SOMEONE MAY YET *CONNECT* THE DEATHS OF IVANOV AND ROSCOE ... THOUGH I *DOUBT* IT.

THE *CIA, MI6,* EVEN THE *KGB* ... *PAH!* THEY'RE SHADOWS OF WHAT THEY *USED* TO BE.

NEVERTHELESS, THE *SOONER* WE FINISH THIS PHASE, THE MORE CHANCE OF REMAINING ... *UNNOTICED.*

WHEN IS THE FINAL BOY *ARRIVING?*

ALEX FRIEND? I'M PICKING HIM UP FROM ENGLAND TOMORROW.

EXCELLENT. YOU WILL TAKE HIM TO *PARIS* ON THE WAY HERE?

IF THAT IS YOUR *WISH,* DOCTOR.

IT IS VERY *MUCH* MY WISH, MRS STELLENBOSCH. WE CAN DO THE PRELIMINARY WORK *THERE.* NOW, WHAT ABOUT THE *SPRINTZ* BOY?

WE STILL NEED A *FEW* MORE DAYS. SHALL I *REMOVE* HIM, SO THAT HE AND ALEX AREN'T HERE AT THE SAME *TIME*?

HMMM... NO, SPRINTZ CAN STAY WITH *US* FOR A FEW MORE DAYS. IT WILL BE ALL RIGHT.

ALEX FRIEND IS AN *EXCELLENT* CATCH FOR US, YOU KNOW.

REALLY? *SUPERMARKETS?*

HIS FATHER ALSO HAS THE *PRIME MINISTER'S* EAR. I AM SURE HIS SON WILL MEET *ALL* OUR EXPECTATIONS.

VERY SOON, WE'LL HAVE ALEX *HERE* AT THE ACADEMY. AND THEN, AT LAST, THE *GEMINI PROJECT* WILL BE *COMPLETE.*

I HADN'T *THOUGHT* OF THAT!

THE TROUBLE IS, I'M NOT REALLY A *FIELD AGENT!*

GET IT?

HAVE YOU GOT ME ANOTHER *NINTENDO?*

NO, THAT'S THE *PROBLEM.* THE ACADEMY DOESN'T *ALLOW* GAMES OF ANY SORT, OR EVEN *COMPUTERS.* THEY SUPPLY ALL THEIR *OWN.*

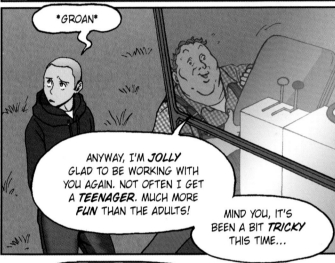

GROAN

ANYWAY, I'M *JOLLY* GLAD TO BE WORKING WITH YOU AGAIN. NOT OFTEN I GET A *TEENAGER.* MUCH MORE *FUN* THAN THE ADULTS!

MIND YOU, IT'S BEEN A BIT *TRICKY* THIS TIME...

NOW, I'M TOLD THERE'S A LOT OF *SNOW* UP ON POINT BLANC, SO YOU'LL NEED *THIS.* KNOW WHAT IT IS?

I'VE BEEN *SKIING* BEFORE, MR SMITHERS.

BUT NOT IN A SUIT LIKE *THIS.* IT'S HIGHLY *INSULATED,* AND ALSO *BULLET-PROOF.*

WOW.

AND THESE ARE *SKI GOGGLES.*

BUT IN CASE YOU HAVE TO BE ANYWHERE AT *NIGHT,* THEY ALSO HAVE AN *INFRARED* MODE.

JUST PRESS THE *SWITCH* AND YOU'LL BE ABLE TO SEE FOR *TWENTY METRES,* EVEN IF THERE'S NO *MOON.*

NOW, YOU'RE NOT ALLOWED *COMPUTERS...*

ABSOLUTELY. MAY I SUGGEST SOME *BEETHOVEN?*

BUT YOU ARE ALLOWED A *SONY DISCMAN,* PROVIDED ALL THE CDS ARE *CLASSICAL.*

SO WHILE PEOPLE ARE *SHOOTING* AT ME IN THE MIDDLE OF THE *NIGHT,* I CAN LISTEN TO MUSIC? *GREAT.*

IT *CONVERTS* THE DISCMAN INTO AN *ELECTRIC* SAW. THE CD IS *DIAMOND-EDGED.* IT'LL CUT THROUGH JUST ABOUT *ANYTHING!*

RRRRRR R

THE *DETONATION*.

YOU SEE, IT'S A SMALL BUT POWERFUL *EXPLOSIVE*. *SEPARATING* THE PIECES AGAIN ACTIVATES THE *SECOND* STAGE,

A TEN-SECOND *COUNTDOWN*. THE BLAST WILL BLOW A HOLE IN ALMOST ANYTHING ... OR *ANYONE*.

JUST SO LONG AS IT DOESN'T BLOW MY *EAR* OFF ...

NO, NO, IT'S *PERFECTLY* SAFE WHILE YOU'RE *WEARING* IT. JUST DON'T TAKE IT *OUT* UNTIL YOU NEED TO *DESTROY* SOMETHING.

GOOD LUCK OLD CHAP!

GOODBYE, MR SMITHERS.

CHUGGA   CHUGGA...

COME BACK IN *ONE PIECE*. I REALLY DO *ENJOY* HAVING YOU AROUND!

CHUGGA   CHUGGA

WHUPPA WHUPPA WHUPPA WHUPPA
HAVERSTOCK HALL
GOOD MORNING! YOU MUST BE MR AND MRS FRIEND!
I'M MRS STELLENBOSCH, ASSISTANT DIRECTOR OF THE ACADEMY!

YES, WELL ... HE WAS *EXPELLED* FROM *ETON* LAST YEAR, AND HE'S BEEN ARRESTED FOR *SHOPLIFTING*. I ... I THINK *DRUGS* MIGHT BE INVOLVED.

I'M AT MY *WIT'S END*. WE HAVE A DAUGHTER, AND SHE'S *PERFECT*, BUT ALEX JUST HANGS AROUND THE HOUSE. HE DOESN'T *READ* OR SHOW ANY INTEREST IN *ANYTHING*.

I UNDERSTAND THAT ALEX HAS BEEN A GREAT SOURCE OF *CONCERN* TO YOU.

THE ACADEMY IS OUR *LAST RESORT*. WE'RE DESPERATELY HOPING YOU CAN SORT HIM OUT.

I'M SURE YOU'VE BEEN *GREAT* PARENTS.

BUT THESE MODERN CHILDREN! IT'S *HEART-BREAKING*, THE WAY SOME OF THEM BEHAVE!

YOU'VE DONE THE *RIGHT* THING, COMING TO US. THE ACADEMY HAS HAD A *REMARKABLE* SUCCESS RATE OVER THE PAST ELEVEN YEARS.

WHAT EXACTLY DO YOU ... *DO?*

WE HAVE OUR *METHODS*. WHEN ALEX COMES HOME, HE'LL BE A *COMPLETELY* DIFFERENT BOY!

WHERE *IS* ALEX, BY THE WAY?

I'M *HERE*. WHO WANTS TO KNOW?

YOU WILL *WRITE* TO US, WON'T YOU?

DUNNO. MAYBE.

DON'T *WORRY*, MRS FRIEND. *WE'LL* TAKE CARE OF HIM FOR YOU.

COME *ALONG* NOW, ALEX!

WHUPPA WHUPPA WHUPPA WHUPPA

THINK SHE *FELL* FOR IT?

LET'S *HOPE* SO ... FOR *ALEX'S* SAKE.

WELL, IF THEY WANT A *NAUGHTY BOY*...

...THAT'S WHAT THEY'LL *GET.*

BRRRING

WHAT?

DINNER IS IN *TEN MINUTES*, ALEX. DON'T FORGET TO WEAR SMART CLOTHES!

HMMM.

AH, *ALEX!*
DID YOU REST WELL?

COME ALONG,
SIT DOWN.

I'VE ALREADY
ORDERED. WHAT
WILL *YOU* HAVE?

I'M NOT
SURE ...

OH, DO YOU
SPEAK *FRENCH?*

ERM ... NO.
NO, I *DON'T.*

THEN YOU MUST
LET *ME* ORDER
FOR YOU.

GARÇON!

UNE SOUPE
DE MOULES,
ET UN BIFTEK AVEC
POMME FRITES,
S'IL VOUS PLAÎT.

SOME *SOUP*
TO START, AND
THEN A *STEAK.*
I'VE *NEVER* MET A
BOY WHO DOESN'T
LIKE STEAK.

MY COUSIN *OLIVER'S*
A VEGETARIAN.

WELL, HE DOESN'T
KNOW WHAT HE'S *MISSING.*
WOULD YOU LIKE A *DRINK?*

YEAH,
A COKE.

MMM? OH ... YES. YES, I THINK I *SHOULD*...

WE DON'T NEED TO LEAVE UNTIL *MIDDAY* TOMORROW. YOU'LL HAVE TIME FOR A VISIT TO THE *LOUVRE*, IF YOU'D LIKE THAT.

NO, PAINTINGS ARE BOR—

NNH!

WOULD YOU LIKE ME TO COME *UP* WITH YOU?

NO...

JUST *TIRED*, I'LL BE ALL RIGHT...

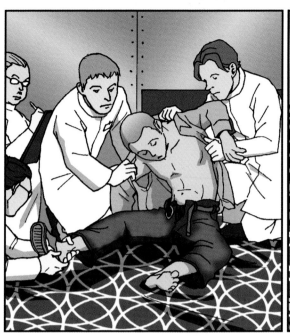

KLIK!

KLIK!

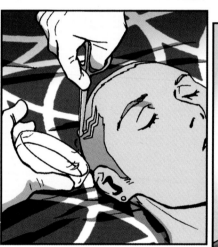

WHIRRRRRR

FRIEND, ALEX
FULL BODY SCAN

BEEP

BEEP

BEEP

BEEP

ZMMMMMM

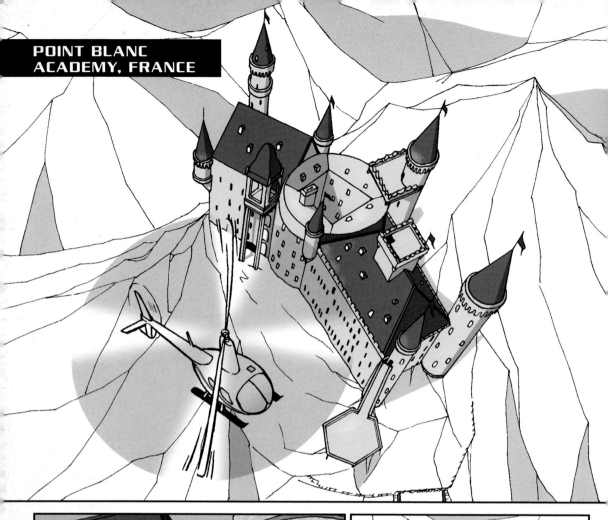

I'LL TAKE YOU DOWN TO MEET THE *DIRECTOR*. YOUR LUGGAGE WILL BE BROUGHT *FOR* YOU.

WE DON'T *USE* THE SKI JUMP, IT'S *FORBIDDEN*. COME DOWN, NOW, OUT OF THE *COLD*.

MIND YOUR STEP.

THESE ARE **CLASSROOMS**. YOU'LL SEE THEM LATER.

THROUGH THE COURTYARD.

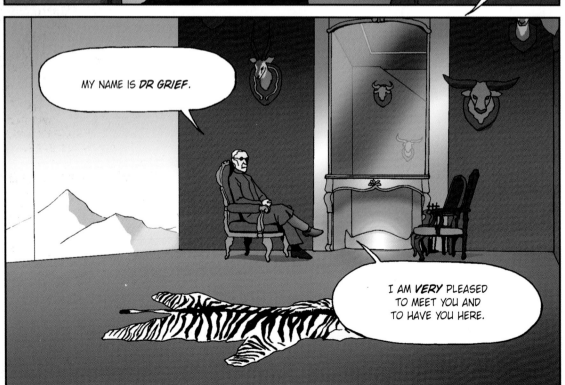

NICE PLACE.

YOU *THINK* SO? THE BUILDING WAS DESIGNED BY A *FRENCHMAN* WHO WAS CERTAINLY THE WORLD'S *WORST* ARCHITECT.

THIS WAS HIS *ONLY* COMMISSION. WHEN THE FIRST OWNERS MOVED IN, THEY HAD HIM *SHOT*.

THERE ARE STILL QUITE A *FEW* PEOPLE HERE WITH *GUNS*.

ALL THE BOYS HERE COME FROM FAMILIES OF GREAT *WEALTH* AND *IMPORTANCE*, LIKE YOURSELF.

WE COULD VERY EASILY BECOME A TARGET FOR *TERRORISTS*, SO THE GUARDS ARE FOR *YOUR* PROTECTION.

THAT'S VERY *KIND*, BUT I DON'T REALLY WANT TO *BE* HERE. SO IF YOU'LL JUST TELL ME HOW I CAN GET DOWN INTO *TOWN*, I'LL CATCH THE NEXT TRAIN HOME.

THERE IS *NO* WAY DOWN INTO TOWN. THE SKIING SEASON IS *OVER*, AND THE DESCENT IS NOW TOO *DANGEROUS*.

THERE IS ONLY THE *HELICOPTER* ... AND THAT WILL TAKE YOU FROM HERE ONLY WHEN *I* SAY SO.

YOU ARE *HERE*, ALEX, BECAUSE YOU HAVE *DISAPPOINTED* YOUR PARENTS.

YOU WERE EXPELLED FROM SCHOOL, YOU HAVE HAD DIFFICULTIES WITH THE *POLICE*—

YOUR **ATTITUDE** IS AS DISPLEASING AS YOUR **APPEARANCE**. IT IS **OUR** JOB TO TURN YOU INTO A BOY OF WHOM YOUR PARENTS CAN BE **PROUD**.

I'M HAPPY AS I AM.

THAT IS OF **NO** RELEVANCE.

THAT WASN'T MY FAULT!

DON'T **INTERRUPT** THE DOCTOR!

FOR THE FIRST COUPLE OF WEEKS HERE,

YOU WILL **ASSIMILATE**.

I'LL **WHAT?**

ASSIMILATE. TO CONFORM ... TO ADAPT ... TO **BECOME LIKE.**

THERE ARE CURRENTLY **SIX** BOYS HERE.

YOU WILL MEET AND SPEND TIME WITH THEM, WITH OPPORTUNITIES FOR **SPORT, SOCIALIZING** AND **READING** IN OUR EXCELLENT LIBRARY. YOU WILL LEARN OUR **METHODS.**

I **HEARD** THAT!

YOU WILL BE **POLITE** TO THE ASSISTANT DIRECTOR!

I WANT TO CALL MY MUM AND DAD.

TELEPHONES ARE **FORBIDDEN.** SO ARE **PERSONAL COMPUTERS,** SO YOU CAN'T **E-MAIL** THEM EITHER. YOU MAY WRITE A **LETTER,** IF YOU LIKE.

UP YOURS.

YOU SHOULD **KNOW**, ALEX, THAT MRS STELLENBOSCH HAS WORKED WITH ME NOW FOR **TWENTY-SIX YEARS**.

WHEN I MET HER, SHE HAD BEEN **MISS SOUTH AFRICA** FIVE YEARS IN A ROW.

A **BEAUTY CONTEST?**

NO. **WEIGHTLIFTING.**

WE ENFORCE **STRICT DISCIPLINE** AT POINT BLANC.

BEDTIME IS TEN O'CLOCK **SHARP**. WE DO NOT TOLERATE **BAD LANGUAGE**. YOU WILL **NOT** CONTACT THE OUTSIDE WORLD WITHOUT OUR **PERMISSION**. YOU WILL **NOT** ATTEMPT TO LEAVE. YOU WILL DO AS YOU ARE TOLD **INSTANTLY**, WITHOUT HESITATION.

FINALLY, YOU ARE PERMITTED **ONLY** IN CERTAIN **PARTS** OF THE BUILDING.

YOU WILL REMAIN ON THE **GROUND** AND **FIRST** FLOORS **ONLY**, WHERE THE BEDROOMS AND CLASSROOMS ARE LOCATED.

THE SECOND AND THIRD FLOORS, **AND** THE BASEMENT, ARE **OUT OF BOUNDS**. THIS IS FOR YOUR **OWN** SAFETY.

GO NOW, AND WAIT **OUTSIDE**. SOMEONE WILL BE ALONG TO **COLLECT** YOU.

WE WILL MAKE YOU INTO WHAT YOUR PARENTS **WANT**, ALEX.

MAYBE THEY DON'T WANT ME AT **ALL**.

WE CAN ARRANGE **THAT** TOO.

HANG ON...

DIETER SPRINTZ? "THE HUNDRED MILLION DOLLAR MAN"?

YEAH. COME ON, THIS WAY.

DOES THIS PLACE REALLY ONLY HAVE SIX BOYS IN IT? IT COULD HOUSE SIXTY.

YEAH. DON'T ASK ME WHY.

ANYWAY, THIS IS THE LIBRARY.

AND THAT'S TOM AND HUGO.

PROBABLY DOING EXTRA MATHS OR SOMETHING.

CREEPS.

YOU KNOW, WHEN I CAME HERE THEY SAID ALL THE BOYS HAD PROBLEMS. I THOUGHT IT WAS GOING TO BE WILD. DO YOU HAVE A CIGARETTE?

I DON'T SMOKE.

TYPICAL.

DINING ROOM.

LIVING ROOM.

A COUPLE OF DAYS AGO I GOT INTO A **FIGHT** WITH TWO OF THEM, JUST FOR THE HELL OF IT. THEY BEAT THE **SNOT** OUT OF ME AND WENT **STRAIGHT** BACK TO THEIR **STUDIES!**

ANYWAY, I **GET** HERE AND IT'S LIKE A **MUSEUM** OR **MONASTERY** OR ... I DON'T KNOW.

EVERYONE'S QUIET, HARD-WORKING, **BORING.** IT'S LIKE GRIEF SUCKED THEIR **BRAINS** OUT WITH A **STRAW.**

WEIRD.

YEAH.

DON'T TRY PLAYING **SNOOKER**, BY THE WAY. THE ROOM'S ON A **SLANT** AND ALL THE BALLS ROLL TO THE SIDE.

COME ON, THE **BEDROOMS** ARE UP HERE. I'LL SHOW YOU YOURS.

DO YOU HAVE THE **KEY?**

NO NEED. THE DOORS **CAN'T** BE **LOCKED.**

HERE YOU GO. THEY'VE PUT YOU NEXT TO ME.

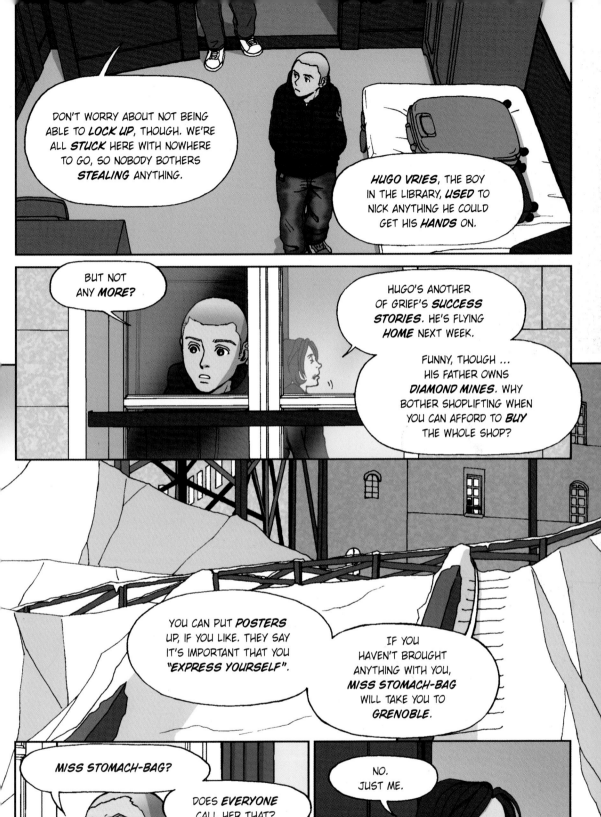

DON'T WORRY ABOUT NOT BEING ABLE TO *LOCK UP*, THOUGH. WE'RE ALL *STUCK* HERE WITH NOWHERE TO GO, SO NOBODY BOTHERS *STEALING* ANYTHING.

HUGO VRIES, THE BOY IN THE LIBRARY, *USED* TO NICK ANYTHING HE COULD GET HIS *HANDS* ON.

BUT NOT ANY *MORE*?

HUGO'S ANOTHER OF GRIEF'S *SUCCESS STORIES*. HE'S FLYING *HOME* NEXT WEEK.

FUNNY, THOUGH ... HIS FATHER OWNS *DIAMOND MINES*. WHY BOTHER SHOPLIFTING WHEN YOU CAN AFFORD TO *BUY* THE WHOLE SHOP?

YOU CAN PUT *POSTERS* UP, IF YOU LIKE. THEY SAY IT'S IMPORTANT THAT YOU *"EXPRESS YOURSELF"*.

IF YOU HAVEN'T BROUGHT ANYTHING WITH YOU, *MISS STOMACH-BAG* WILL TAKE YOU TO *GRENOBLE*.

MISS STOMACH-BAG?

DOES *EVERYONE* CALL HER THAT?

NO. JUST ME.

ALEX, THIS IS A DEEPLY *WEIRD* PLACE. I'VE BEEN TO A *LOT* OF SCHOOLS, BECAUSE I'VE BEEN *THROWN OUT* OF A LOT OF SCHOOLS ... BUT THIS IS THE *PITS*.

THEY SAID THEY WANT US TO *ASSIMILATE*.

THAT'S *THEIR* WORD FOR IT, SURE. BUT THIS PLACE ... THEY *CALL* IT A SCHOOL, BUT IT'S MORE LIKE BEING IN A *PRISON*. YOU SAW THE GUARDS?

I THOUGHT THEY WERE HERE TO *PROTECT* US.

I'VE BEEN HERE SIX WEEKS, AND HARDLY EVEN HAD ANY *LESSONS*. THEY HAVE *MUSIC* EVENINGS, AND *DISCUSSION* EVENINGS, AND THEY TRY TO GET ME TO *READ*, BUT OTHERWISE I'VE BEEN LEFT ON MY OWN.

THEN YOU'RE A BIGGER *IDIOT* THAN I THOUGHT.

THERE ARE ABOUT *THIRTY* OF THEM! FOR *SEVEN KIDS*!

THAT'S NOT PROTECTION, THAT'S *INTIMIDATION*.

SORRY,

I SHOULDN'T LOSE MY *TEMPER*. IT'D JUST BE NICE TO THINK *SOMEONE'S* FINALLY ARRIVED THAT I CAN *RELATE* TO.

MAYBE YOU *CAN*.

YEAH, BUT FOR *HOW LONG*?

SEE YOU LATER, ALEX.

HMMM.

NO.
TOO SOON.

BRRRING   BRRRING

DINNER *ALREADY?*
TIME FLIES...

WHAT ON EARTH...?

HUGO VRIES (14) Dutch, lives in Amsterdam. Father's name: Rudi, owns diamond mines. Speaks little English. Reads and plays guitar. Very solitary. Sent to PB for shoplifting and arson.

TOM McMORIN (14) Canadian, from Vancouver. Parents divorced. Mother runs media empire (newspapers, TV). Well-built, chess player. Car thefts and drunken driving.

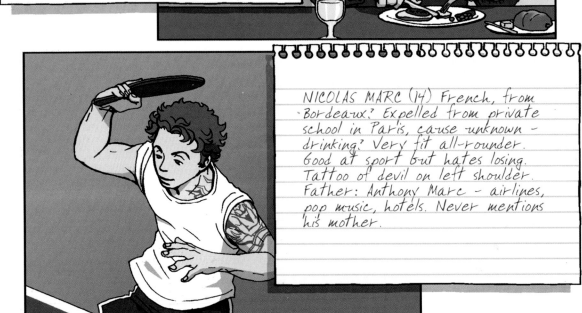

NICOLAS MARC (14) French, from Bordeaux? Expelled from private school in Paris, cause unknown – drinking? Very fit all-rounder. Good at sport but hates losing. Tattoo of devil on left shoulder. Father: Anthony Marc – airlines, pop music, hotels. Never mentions his mother.

CASSIAN JAMES (14) American. Mother: Jill, studio chief in Hollywood. Parents divorced. Loud voice. Swears a lot. Plays jazz piano. Expelled from three schools. Various drug offences - sent to PB after smuggling arrest but won't talk about it now. One of the kids who beat up James. Stronger than he looks.

JOE CANTERBURY (14) American. Spends a lot of time with Cassian (helped him with James). Mother (name unknown) New York senator. Father something big at the Pentagon. Vandalism, truancy, shoplifting. Sent to PB after stealing and smashing up car. Vegetarian. Permanently chewing gum. Has he given up smoking?

JAMES SPRINTZ (14) German, lives in Düsseldorf. Father: Dieter Sprintz, banker, well-known financier (the One Hundred Million Dollar Man). Mother living in England. Expelled for wounding a teacher with an air pistol. My only friend at PB! And the only one who really hates it here.

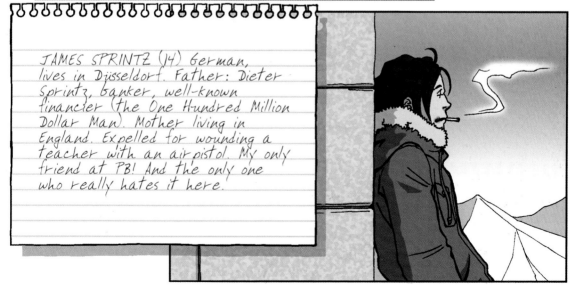

THEY'RE **ALL** FOURTEEN ... **MOST** OF THEM HAVE DIVORCED PARENTS ...

ALL OF THEM HAVE **WEALTHY** PARENTS...

FROM ALL OVER THE **WORLD**, ALL SUCCESSFUL IN **DIFFERENT** AREAS...

...BUT SO **WHAT?** WHAT MAKES THEM DIFFERENT FROM **OTHER** KIDS LIKE THEM?

BRRRING BRRRING

BRRRING BRRRING

YEAH, YEAH...

BRRRING BRRRING BRRRING

...ates it here.

Brainwashing?

WILL YOU BE JOINING US FOR *LATIN* AFTER LUNCH, ALEX?

GET LOST.

WHAT'S THE MATTER, LATIN TOO *ADVANCED* FOR YOU? PERHAPS YOU'D PREFER YOUR *TIMES TABLES*, THAT SHOULD BE *EASY* ENOUGH!

HA HA HA!

I THOUGHT YOU WERE SUPPOSED TO BE A *HARD REBEL*, CASSIAN. BUT *LOOK* AT YOU, SUCKING UP TO A *PATHETIC OLD MAN!*

DON'T YOU *TALK* ABOUT THE DOCTOR LIKE THAT! HE'S A *GENIUS!*

COME ON, LET'S GO AND GET SOME *FRESH AIR*. I FEEL *SICK*.

POINT
BLANC

THIS WAY.

WHAT THE...?

ALEX! ARE YOU **COMING?**

IT'S GONE...

WHAT'S GONE?

...I DON'T **KNOW.** NOTHING.

MY EYES MUST BE PLAYING **TRICKS** ON ME.

I CAN **TRUST** YOU, ALEX, BECAUSE YOU'VE ONLY JUST **GOT** HERE. **HE** HASN'T GOT TO YOU YET.

ARE YOU GOING TO RUN AWAY?

BUT IF YOU **STAY**, YOU'LL END UP LIKE THE OTHERS. "MODEL STUDENTS" ... HOW **APPROPRIATE**. IT'S LIKE THEY'RE ALL MADE OUT OF **PLASTICENE!**

WELL, I'M **NOT** GOING TO LET HIM DO THAT TO **ME**.

WHO NEEDS TO **RUN?** I'M GOING TO **SKI**.

I KNOW GRIEF SAYS IT'S TOO **DANGEROUS**. BUT HE **WOULD**, WOULDN'T HE? YEAH, IT'S ALL **BLACK RUNS** ALL THE WAY DOWN, AND THERE'LL BE TONS OF **MOGULS–**

WON'T THE SNOW HAVE **MELTED?** SKI SEASON'S **OVER**.

ONLY FURTHER DOWN. I'VE **BEEN** RIGHT DOWN TO THE BOTTOM. I DID IT THE FIRST WEEK I WAS **HERE**.

ALL THE SLOPES RUN INTO A SINGLE VALLEY, **LA VALLÉE DE FER**. YOU CAN'T SKI AS FAR AS THE **TOWN**, BECAUSE THERE'SA **TRAIN TRACK** THAT CUTS ACROSS.

BUT IF I CAN GET **THAT** FAR, I RECKON I CAN **WALK** THE REST OF THE WAY.

AND THEN WHAT?

A TRAIN TO *DÜSSELDORF*. IF FATHER TRIES TO SEND ME *BACK* HERE, I'LL GO TO MY *MUM* IN ENGLAND. AND IF *SHE* DOESN'T WANT ME, I'VE GOT *FRIENDS* IN PARIS AND BERLIN.

ALL I KNOW IS, I'VE GOT TO *SPLIT*. IF YOU KNOW WHAT'S *GOOD* FOR YOU, *YOU'LL* COME TOO.

I DON'T HAVE ANY *SKIS*.

NOR DO *I*. GRIEF'S GOT THEM ALL *LOCKED UP* SOMEWHERE.

ON THE THIRD FLOOR?

MAYBE. BUT I'LL *FIND* THEM. AND THEN I'M *OUT* OF HERE.

COME *WITH* ME, ALEX.

NO ... I'M *SORRY*. YOU GO, AND *GOOD LUCK* TO YOU. BUT I'LL STICK IT OUT A BIT LONGER.

I DON'T WANT TO BREAK MY *NECK*.

WELL, THAT'S *YOUR* LOOKOUT.

I'LL SEND YOU A *POSTCARD*.

HAVE YOU EVER WONDERED WHAT GOES *ON* UP THERE?

NO. I SUPPOSE IT'S WHERE THE *GUARDS* LIVE.

TWO WHOLE FLOORS, JUST FOR *THEM*?

THERE'S A *BASEMENT* AS WELL. AND DR GRIEF'S ROOMS ... I WONDER IF HE *SLEEPS* WITH MISS STOMACH-BAG?

IMAGINE THAT, *DARTH VADER* AND *KING KONG!*

HA HA! GROSS!

KLIK

LOCKED, BUT...?

HMMM...

...TIME FOR SOME *BEETHOVEN.*

BEEP

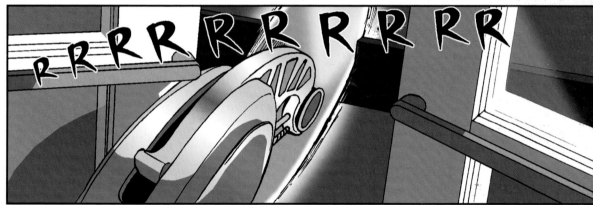

RRRRRRRRRR

RR RR R...

...SO KALT DASS EINEM ALLES *ABFRIERT*...

DAS *STIMMT*...

SLAM!

KOF! KOF!

DAMN.

KLANG
KLANG

METAL?
THAT'S WEIRD.

GOOD MORNING, MRS STELLENBOSCH!

GOOD MORNING, BOYS. TODAY'S LESSONS START WITH *HISTORY*, IN THE *TOWER ROOM* IN TEN MINUTES.

TODAY WE'RE LOOKING AT THE LIFE OF A VERY INTERESTING MAN ... *ADOLF HITLER*.

JAMES, I HOPE YOU'RE GOING TO *JOIN* US?

YES, MRS STELLENBOSCH.

YOU'RE ACTUALLY *GOING* TO *LESSONS*?

WHY *NOT?* I'M STUCK HERE, AND THERE ISN'T MUCH *ELSE* TO DO. MAYBE I SHOULD HAVE GONE TO LESSONS *BEFORE*.

YOU SHOULDN'T BE SO *NEGATIVE*, ALEX. YOU'RE WASTING YOUR *TIME*.

A-HA.

I *THOUGHT* SO.

AND IF THERE'S A *CHIMNEY*...

...THERE MIGHT BE OTHER *FIREPLACES* FURTHER UP.

MMF!

A **WINDOW** WHERE THERE SHOULD BE DOORS! SO I **AM** ON THE THIRD FLOOR AFTER ALL...

NO, WAIT...

THIS IS DIFFERENT.

...BUT IT'S AN EXACT **REPLICA** OF THE GROUND FLOOR!

SO WHY KEEP IT **SECRET?** IT DOESN'T MAKE ANY **SENSE.**

NOW, THEN...

DOWNSTAIRS, THIS WOULD BE THE **LIBRARY**.

OH!

EVEN THE *BOOKS* ARE THE SAME...

LIBRARY

IS IT *ALL* LIKE THIS?

WAIT, *THIS* IS NEW.

IT CAN'T BE *THIS* LIBRARY, BECAUSE *I'M* NOT IN THE PICTURE ... IT MUST BE THE ONE *DOWNSTAIRS*.

SO YOU CAN SIT IN ONE AND *WATCH* THE OTHER.

BUT *WHY*? WHAT'S THE *POINT*?

JAMES' ROOM...

EXACTLY THE SAME.

WHAT ABOUT *MINE?*

OH, NO.

NO, WAIT...

THE *DISCMAN,* MY *SUITCASE...*

THEY'RE NOT HERE. THERE'S NOTHING *PERSONAL.*

WHY *NOT?* WHAT ARE THEY *WAITING* FOR?

SLAM

...YOU HAVE **COMPLETED** THE WORK. I AM **GRATEFUL** TO YOU, MR BAXTER.

THANK YOU, DR GRIEF.

SO, I HOPE YOU'RE **PLEASED** WITH THE LAST OPERATION.

ENTIRELY. I SAW HIM AS SOON AS THE **BANDAGES** CAME OFF.

YOU HAVE DONE EXTREMELY WELL.

I ALWAYS **WAS** THE BEST. BUT THAT'S WHAT YOU **PAID** FOR.

AND WHILE WE'RE **ON** THAT SUBJECT, MAYBE WE SHOULD TALK ABOUT MY FINAL **PAYMENT?**

YOU HAVE **ALREADY** BEEN PAID **ONE MILLION** AMERICAN DOLLARS, MR BAXTER.

OF **COURSE**, DR GRIEF. BUT I THOUGHT YOU MIGHT LIKE TO CONSIDER A LITTLE ... **BONUS.**

WE HAD AN **AGREEMENT.**

FOR MY **WORK**, YES. MY **SILENCE** IS ANOTHER MATTER.

I WAS THINKING ANOTHER **QUARTER MILLION**. GIVEN THE SIZE OF YOUR **GEMINI PROJECT**, IT'S NOT SO MUCH TO ASK.

THEN I'LL RETIRE TO **SPAIN** AND YOU'LL NEVER HEAR FROM ME AGAIN, I **PROMISE.**

I WILL **NEVER** HEAR FROM YOU **AGAIN** ... YES.

YES, I THINK THAT IS A **GOOD IDEA.**

PTUI!

THIS IS *GRIEF*.

I HAVE SOME *GARBAGE* IN THE OPERATING THEATRE THAT NEEDS TO BE REMOVED. INFORM THE *DISPOSAL TEAM*.

SHHHHHUNK

SHHHHHHUNK

HIER! JA, IN DER *WÄSCHEREI!*

WAS HAT DER DA GEMACHT?

KANNST DU DIR DAS NICHT *DENKEN?*

SHHHUNK

GROUND FLOOR, GROUND FLOOR ... OF COURSE, IT'S *"REZ-DE-CHAUSSÉE"*.

3
2
1
R
S

"R"!

KLIK!

HIER IST DER *MÜLL*.

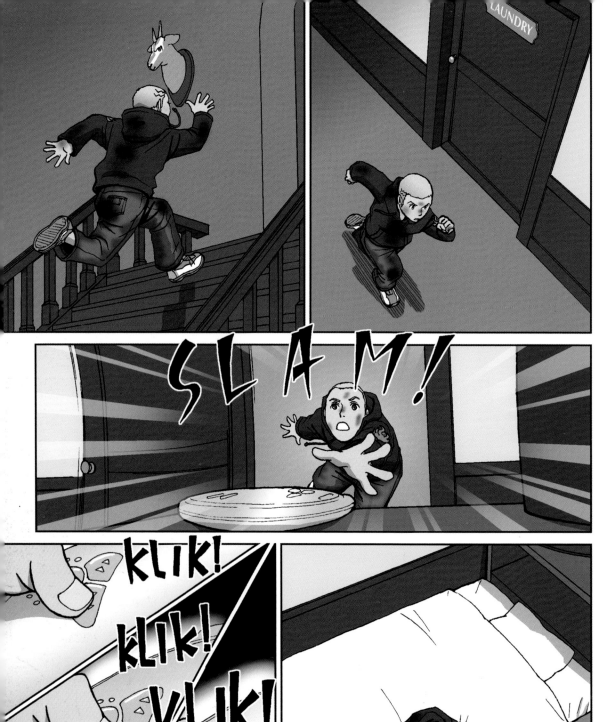

SLAM!

KLIK!

KLIK!

KLIK!

WE'VE HEARD FROM *ALEX*.

HE SENT THE *PANIC SIGNAL* FROM HIS PORTABLE SATELLITE TRANSMITTER THIS MORNING, AT *1027 HOURS* HIS TIME.

MOST URGENT

WE HAVE TO PULL HIM *OUT*.

I *WONDER*. ALEX HAS BEEN AT POINT BLANC FOR JUST *ONE WEEK*, YES? AND WE KNOW HE DIDN'T WANT TO GO IN THE *FIRST* PLACE.

HE *SENT* THE SIGNAL, ALAN! THAT MEANS HE'S EITHER *FOUND* SOMETHING OR HE'S IN *DANGER*. EITHER WAY, WE CAN'T JUST SIT BACK AND DO *NOTHING!*

ALEX MAY NO LONGER BE *100%* RELIABLE.

I WASN'T *SUGGESTING* THAT.

THAT'S NOT THE POINT. ALEX IS *SPECIAL*.

YOU SEEM TO BE FORMING QUITE AN *ATTACHMENT* TO ALEX, MRS JONES. YOU HAVE CHILDREN OF YOUR *OWN*, DON'T YOU?

WE CAN'T GO **BLUNDERING** INTO POINT BLANC WITHOUT **FIRM** INFORMATION.

THIS IS **FRANCE** WE'RE TALKING ABOUT. IF WE'RE SEEN TO BE INVADING THEIR **TERRITORY** THEY'LL KICK UP ONE **HELL** OF A FUSS.

BESIDES, GRIEF HAS BOYS FROM SOME OF THE **WEALTHIEST** FAMILIES IN THE **WORLD**. WE GO **STORMING IN** AND THE WHOLE THING COULD BLOW UP INTO A **MAJOR INTERNATIONAL INCIDENT**.

ALEX MAY HAVE THE **PROOF** YOU NEED TO **CONNECT** GRIEF WITH THE DEATHS OF **ROSCOE** AND **IVANOV**.

AND HE MAY **NOT**.

...

A **TWENTY-FOUR HOUR DELAY** SHOULDN'T MAKE MUCH DIFFERENCE. WE'LL PUT AN **SAS UNIT** ON STANDBY. IF ALEX **IS** IN TROUBLE, WE'LL FIND OUT SOON ENOUGH.

AND IT COULD PLAY TO OUR **FAVOUR** IF HE'S MANAGED TO STIR THINGS **UP**. FORCE GRIEF TO SHOW HIS **HAND**.

AND IF ALEX CONTACTS US **AGAIN?**

THEN WE'LL GO IN.

ASSUMING HE'S NOT ALREADY **DEAD**.

SLAM!

HEY, ALEX! COMING TO *LATIN* THIS MORNING?

LATIN'S A WASTE OF TIME.

IS *THAT* WHAT YOU THINK?

YOU'RE THE ONE WHO'S *WASTING* HIS *TIME*, ALEX.

WHATEVER. YOU ENJOY IT.

COME ON, THERE *MUST* BE A WAY TO OPEN IT FROM *THIS* SIDE, TOO...

HMMM. A *RAISED* BUTTON...

KLIK!

WOAH.

WHRRRRRr

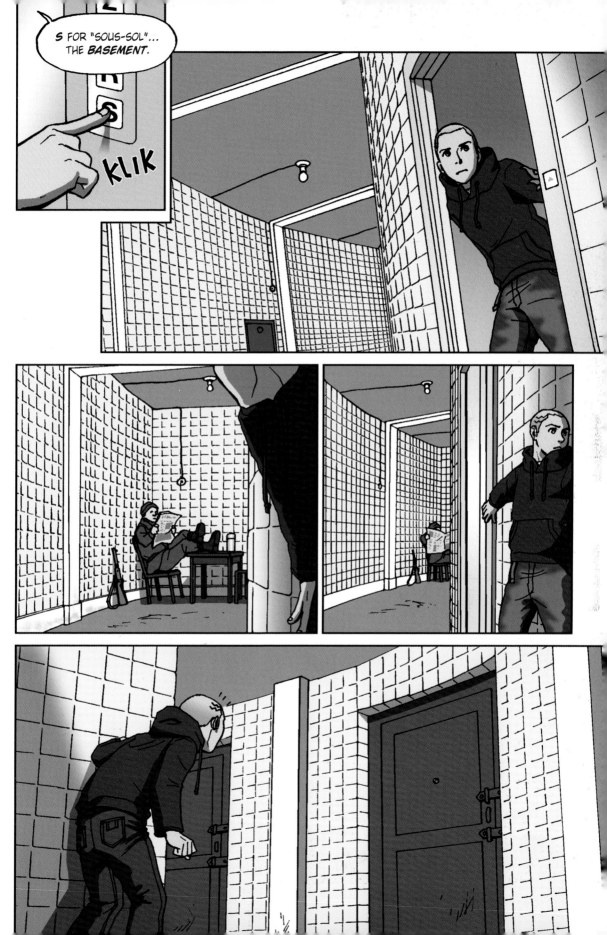

MMMMMMM

COME ON, COME ON...

ALEX! WHAT ARE YOU DOING HERE?

SHHH, KEEP YOUR VOICE DOWN! WE HAVEN'T GOT MUCH TIME ... WHAT HAPPENED TO YOU?

THEY CAME THE NIGHT BEFORE LAST. DRAGGED ME OUT OF BED AND INTO THE LIBRARY. THERE'S A LIFT—

BEHIND THE ARMOUR, I KNOW. WHAT DID THEY SAY?

NOTHING. NO ONE WOULD TELL ME WHAT WAS GOING ON, THEY JUST THREW ME IN HERE!

ALL OF US. I DON'T KNOW HOW OR WHY, BUT THAT'S WHAT'S GOING DOWN. I'VE BEEN HERE FOR MONTHS.

I'M PAUL, BY THE WAY. PAUL ROSCOE.

YOU'VE BEEN HERE FOR TWO DAYS? BUT I JUST SAW YOU UPSTAIRS, HAVING BREAKFAST!

THEY'VE MADE DUPLICATES OF US, DUDE.

ROSCOE? ARE YOU *MICHAEL* ROSCOE'S SON?

YEAH, WHY?

...NOTHING.

HOW DID YOU GET *DOWN* HERE, ALEX? WHAT'S GOING *ON?*

ALL RIGHT, LISTEN CAREFULLY.

MY NAME *ISN'T* ALEX FRIEND, IT'S *ALEX RIDER.* I WAS SENT HERE BY *MI6.* AND EVERYTHING'S GOING TO BE OK. THEY'RE SENDING PEOPLE IN TO *FREE* YOU ALL.

YOU'RE ... A *SPY?*

SORT OF. I SUPPOSE.

DUDE, WHAT ARE WE *WAITING* FOR? LET'S GET *OUTTA* HERE!

NO!

YOU'VE GOT TO *WAIT.* THERE'S NO WAY DOWN THE *MOUNTAIN.*

STAY HERE FOR NOW AND I'LL COME BACK WITH HELP, I *PROMISE.* IT'S THE *ONLY* WAY.

I'LL COME *BACK,* I...

...PROMISE.

BUT I *CAN'T—*

YOU *HAVE* TO. *TRUST* ME, PAUL. I'M GOING TO LOCK YOU BACK IN, SO NOBODY WILL KNOW I'VE *BEEN* HERE. BUT IT WON'T BE FOR *LONG.*

UNH!

"HIRED"?

HAAAAHAHAHA!

HAH

YOU HAVE **NO IDEA** WHAT YOU'VE SEEN, DO YOU?

YOUR LITTLE MIND CANNOT **BEGIN** TO ENCOMPASS WHAT **I** HAVE ACHIEVED!

LISTEN **CAREFULLY**, ALEX, AND I SHALL DESCRIBE TO YOU THE **GEMINI PROJECT**.

WHEN YOU GO SCREAMING TO YOUR **DEATH**, YOU WILL UNDERSTAND THAT YOU COULD **NEVER** HOPE TO BEAT A MAN SUCH AS **I**. PERHAPS THAT WILL MAKE DYING **EASIER** FOR YOU.

I AM FROM **SOUTH AFRICA**.

THE ANIMALS IN THIS BUILDING ARE **SOUVENIRS** OF MY TIME THERE, ALL SHOT ON **SAFARI**.

I STILL MISS MY COUNTRY. IT IS THE MOST **BEAUTIFUL** ON THE PLANET.

IN FACT, I WAS ONE OF ITS **FOREMOST BIOCHEMISTS**.

FROM THE UNIVERSITY OF JOHANNESBURG, VIA THE **CYCLOPS INSTITUTE** IN PRETORIA, I EVENTUALLY BECAME **MINISTER FOR SCIENCE**.

WHEN YOU SAID YOU WERE GOING TO **KILL** ME, I DIDN'T REALIZE YOU MEANT BY **BORING** ME TO DEATH.

UNH!

ENOUGH.

LET HIM *HAVE* HIS LITTLE JOKE. THERE WILL BE PLENTY OF *PAIN* FOR HIM *LATER*.

ONCE, ALEX, THE *WHITE PEOPLE* OF SOUTH AFRICA RULED *EVERYTHING*.

UNDER THE LAWS THE REST OF THE WORLD CALLED *APARTHEID*, BLACK PEOPLE COULD NOT *LIVE NEAR* WHITE PEOPLE. THEY COULD NOT *MARRY* WHITE PEOPLE. THEY HAD SEPARATE *TOILETS*, *RESTAURANTS*, *BARS*... THEY HAD TO CARRY *PASSES*, AND WERE TREATED LIKE *ANIMALS*.

YEAH. IT WAS *DISGUSTING*.

NO!

IT WAS *PERFECT!*

BUT AS TIME PASSED, I SAW IT WOULD BE *SHORT-LIVED*.

THE REST OF THE WORLD WAS *GANGING UP* ON US. I FORESAW THE DAY THAT A *CRIMINAL* LIKE *NELSON MANDELA* COULD TAKE POWER!

HOW **WEAK** AND **PATHETIC** THE WORLD WAS BECOMING ... **DETERMINED** TO GIVE AWAY A **GREAT** COUNTRY LIKE MINE TO PEOPLE WHO HAD **NO IDEA** HOW TO RUN IT.

OH, GREAT. ANOTHER **WANNABE WORLD CONQUEROR.**

OOF!

I LOOKED **AROUND** AND SAW THAT THE PEOPLE OF AMERICA AND EUROPE HAD BECOME **STUPID** AND **WEAK**. THE FALL OF THE **BERLIN WALL** ONLY MADE THINGS WORSE. SOON, EVEN **RUSSIA** WAS INFECTED WITH THE SAME DISEASE.

AND I THOUGHT TO MYSELF, HOW MUCH **STRONGER** THE WORLD WOULD BE IF **I** RULED IT. HOW MUCH **BETTER.**

ON THE **CONTRARY,** IT HAS BEEN THE AMBITION OF VERY **FEW** MEN TO RULE THE ENTIRE WORLD. HITLER, NAPOLEON, STALIN ... GREAT MEN, **REMARKABLE** MEN!

MEN LIKE **ME!**

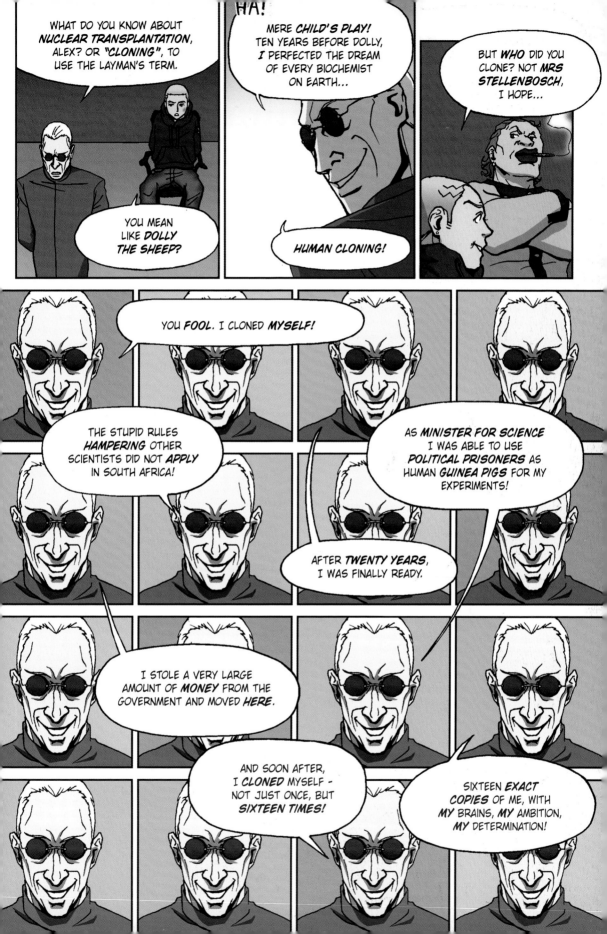

FIFTEEN OF THE WORLD'S MOST **PROMISING** CHILDREN CAME HERE TO POINT BLANC, AND WERE **REPLACED** WITH SURGICALLY ALTERED **CLONES** OF MYSELF.

SURGICALLY ALTERED? THAT MAN, **BAXTER**...

YOU REALLY **HAVE** BEEN BUSY, ALEX.

BAXTER WAS A HARLEY STREET **PLASTIC SURGEON** WITH GAMBLING DEBTS. IT WAS HIS JOB TO **OPERATE** ON MY FAMILY. TO ALTER THEIR **SKIN COLOUR, FACES,** EVEN THEIR **BODIES**.

FROM THEIR **ARRIVAL**, THE BOYS WERE KEPT UNDER **OBSERVATION**.

MY DOUBLES **WATCHED** THEIR TARGETS TO LEARN THEIR MANNERISMS AND HABITS, EVEN THEIR **VOICES**.

BUT ANY PARENT WOULD KNOW IT **WASN'T** THEIR SON, EVEN IF HE **LOOKED** THE SAME!

WRONG!

THESE ARE BUSY PEOPLE, WITH **NO TIME** FOR THEIR CHILDREN. THEY SENT THEIR BOYS HERE BECAUSE THEY **WANTED** THEM TO CHANGE!

NATURE IS ALSO ON OUR SIDE. DURING AN ABSENCE OF SIX WEEKS, A FOURTEEN-YEAR-OLD BOY CAN CHANGE **REMARKABLY**.

HE MAY RETURN HOME **TALLER, FATTER, THINNER ...** EVEN HIS **VOICE** WILL HAVE CHANGED. AND PARENTS WILL SIMPLY SAY:

MY, HOW YOU'VE **GROWN!**

ROSCOE DID NOT BELIEVE WHAT HE SAW. NEITHER DID THAT IDIOT RUSSIAN, *GENERAL IVANOV*. THEY DID NOT GUESS WHAT *REALLY* HAPPENED, BUT THEY KNEW *SOMETHING* WAS WRONG.

BUT *ROSCOE* NOTICED, DIDN'T HE? THAT'S WHY YOU HAD HIM *KILLED*.

STILL, TWO OUT OF SIXTEEN IS *NOT* SUCH A CATASTROPHE.

GEMINI HAS BEEN AN *OUTSTANDING* SUCCESS. THE LAST OF THE CHILDREN WILL *RETURN* TO THEIR FAMILIES IN A FEW DAY'S TIME.

OF COURSE, I MUST *DISPOSE* OF THE *ORIGINALS*. THEY WILL DIE *PAINLESSLY*.

BUT NOT *YOU*, ALEX RIDER.

TOMORROW'S FIRST LESSON IS *DOUBLE BIOLOGY*. MY CHILDREN RECENTLY ASKED TO SEE A *HUMAN DISSECTION*. TOMORROW, I WILL *GRANT* THEIR WISH.

THROW HIM IN ONE OF THE *HIGH SECURITY* CELLS!

WE SHALL *NOT* USE *ANAESTHETIC*. I EXPECT IT WILL BE *VERY PAINFUL* FOR YOU.

TAKE HIS *BELT*, *SHOELACES* AND EVERYTHING IN HIS *POCKETS*. HERR GRIEF SUSPECTS THE BOY MAY ATTEMPT *SUICIDE*.

YEAH, RIGHT. NOT UNLESS I COULD TAKE HIM *WITH* ME.

THIS IS ALL *POINTLESS*, YOU KNOW! *MI6* WILL BE HERE *ANY MINUTE*!

SLAM!

1100 HOURS

ANY MINUTE...

1300 HOURS

1500 HOURS

1700 HOURS

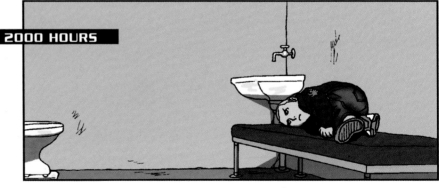

2000 HOURS

2300 HOURS

...

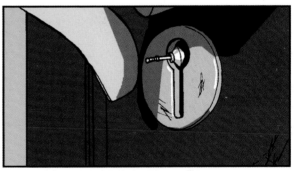

FIRST FLOOR ...
WHERE *AM* I?

THE *LAUNDRY*.

HMMM ...
THAT GIVES ME
AN *IDEA*.

ALL STILL HERE,

PHEW!

LUCKY THEY DIDN'T BOTHER *REPAIRING* THE *WINDOW*...

HE'S *IMPROVISED* SOME KIND OF *SLEIGH* OR *TOBOGGAN*. PERHAPS HE'S NOT SUCH AN *IDIOT* AFTER ALL.

I WANT TWO MEN ON *SNOWMOBILES* TO FOLLOW HIM DOWN. *NOW!*

WHAT ABOUT THE UNIT AT THE *FOOT* OF THE *MOUNTAIN?* WHATEVER HE'S USING, HE'LL BE UNABLE TO CROSS THE *RAILWAY LINE* INTO *LA VALLÉE DE FER.*

TRUE. VERY WELL, HAVE OUR MEN IN THE VAN READY THE *MACHINE GUN.*

ALEX RIDER WILL BE A *SITTING DUCK.*

I WOULD HAVE LIKED TO *WATCH* HIM DIE, BUT NEVER MIND. LET US RETURN TO *BED.*

AND I WILL SEE BOTH OF *YOU* IN MY OFFICE TOMORROW MORNING.

...VRRRRRM

WHAT THE...?

UH OH...

VRRRR RRM

FEUER!

WOOOAH!

BRAKKA BRAKKA

BRAKKA BRAKKA

WARTE ... NICHT SCHIESSEN BIS ER *NÄHER* IST!

HIER KOMMT DER JUNGE.

LA VALLÉE DE FER...

...AND THERE ARE THE *TRAIN TRACKS* JAMES MENTIONED.

FEUER!

BRAKKA

BRAKKA

BRAKKA

WHUMP

WOOO-HOO!

HA HA!

SO LONG...

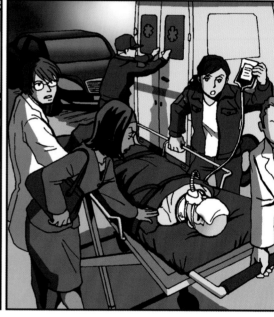

FRAU STELLENBOSCH?
ICH HABE *GUTE*
NACHRICHTEN
FÜR SIE...

I AM *EVA STELLENBOSCH*, ASSISTANT DIRECTOR OF *POINT BLANC ACADEMY*.

I UNDERSTAND ONE OF OUR STUDENTS, *ALEX FRIEND*, WAS BROUGHT HERE THIS MORNING.

AH, YES. TAKE A *SEAT*, MRS STELLENBOSCH. THE DOCTOR WILL BE OUT IN A *MOMENT*.

SNIFF

MADAME STELLENBOSCH?

PLEASE REMAIN *SEATED*, MADAME.

YOU MUST UNDERSTAND, ALEX TRIED TO *SNOWBOARD* DOWN THE MOUNTAIN AT *NIGHT*. HE COLLIDED WITH A TRAIN AT *HIGH SPEED*...

HE BROKE BOTH *ARMS*, HIS *COLLARBONE* AND ONE OF HIS *LEGS*. HIS *SKULL* WAS *FRACTURED*. WE OPERATED AS SOON AS WE COULD, BUT THERE WAS *MASSIVE INTERNAL BLEEDING* AND HE WENT INTO *SHOCK*.

I'M *SORRY*, MADAME. ALEX FRIEND IS *DEAD*.

I ... I MUST INFORM HIS FAMILY.

IS HE SWISS?

NO ... NO, HE IS *ENGLISH*. HIS FATHER, SIR DAVID ... I'LL HAVE TO *TELL* HIM.

THANK YOU, DOCTOR. I'M SURE YOU DID *EVERYTHING* YOU COULD.

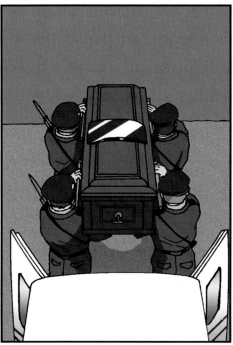

YOU KNOW, YOU'RE *LUCKY* TO BE *ALIVE*. YOU SHOULD HAVE AT LEAST BROKEN *SOMETHING*.

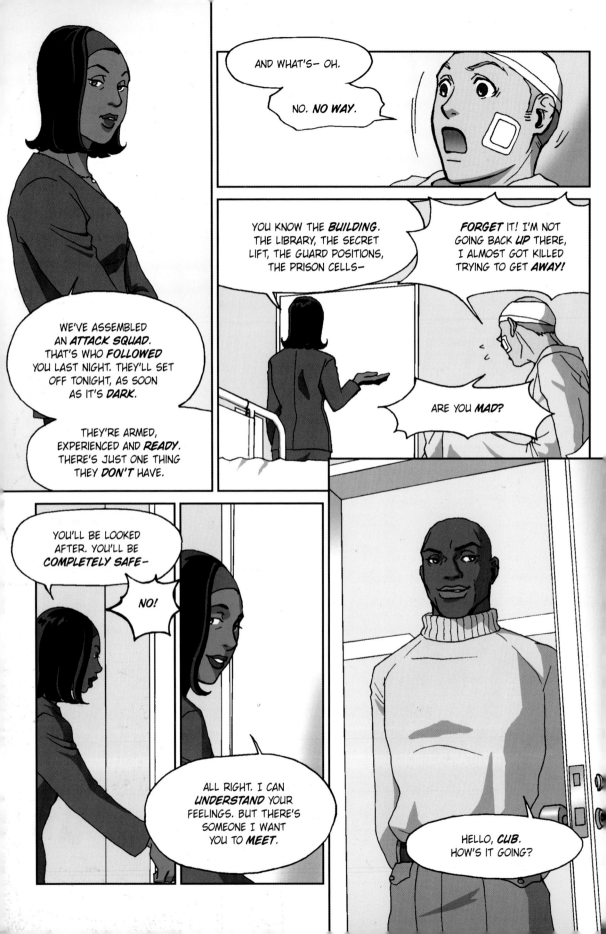

WOLF! WHAT ARE **YOU** DOING HERE?

THEY CALLED ME IN TO **CLEAR UP** THE MESS **YOU** LEFT BEHIND.

SORRY I DIDN'T BRING YOU **FLOWERS** AND **GRAPES**.

ALEX HAS DONE A **VERY** GOOD JOB SO FAR. BUT THERE ARE STILL **FIFTEEN** YOUNG **PRISONERS** AT POINT BLANC, AND OUR PRIORITY IS TO **SAVE** THEM.

ALEX SAYS THERE ARE ABOUT **THIRTY** GUARDS IN AND AROUND THE SCHOOL.

THE **ONLY** CHANCE THOSE BOYS HAVE IS FOR AN **SAS UNIT** TO BREAK IN.

SO WHERE WERE **YOU** WHEN I WAS BEING CHASED DOWN THE MOUNTAIN BY **HOMICIDAL SNOWMOBILE RIDERS**?

YOU SEEMED TO BE DOING FINE ON YOUR **OWN**.

AND THAT UNIT WILL BE COMMANDED BY **WOLF**.

WHERE DOES THE **BOY** COME INTO THIS?

ALEX **KNOWS** THE SCHOOL, THE POSITION OF THE GUARDS AND THE LOCATION OF THE **PRISON CELLS**. HE CAN LEAD YOU TO THE LIFT—

NO.

HE CAN TELL US **EVERYTHING** WE NEED TO KNOW RIGHT **HERE** AND **NOW**.

TWO KILOMETRES
NORTH OF POINT BLANC

GUARDS?

TWO PATROLLING. ONE ON THE ROOF.

THEN LET'S TAKE HIM OUT FIRST.

SWEET DREAMS.

ONE DOWN.

SURE. ONLY ABOUT *TWENTY-NINE* TO GO...

MOVE OUT.

UNH!

WHERE'S THIS *LIFT?*

THE *LIBRARY.*
FOLLOW ME.

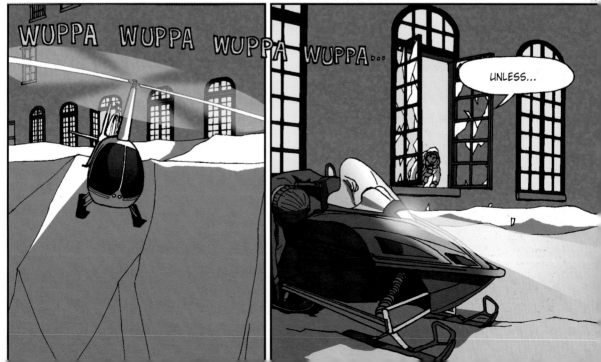

IT SEEMS WE OWE YOU A DEBT OF *THANKS*.

YOU DON'T OWE ME *ANYTHING*.

LIVERPOOL STREET
TWO DAYS LATER

RUBBISH. YOU HAVE CHANGED THE VERY *FUTURE* OF THIS PLANET. GRIEF'S ... *OFFSPRING* ... COULD HAVE CAUSED *MANY* PROBLEMS.

BUT WE HAVE ALL FIFTEEN OF THEM UNDER *LOCK AND KEY*, NOW. THEY WERE *TRACED* AND *ARRESTED* BY THE INTELLIGENCE SERVICES OF EACH COUNTRY WHERE THEY *LIVED*.

OF COURSE, WE'VE HUSHED IT *UP*. CLONING *SHEEP* IS ONE THING, BUT *HUMAN BEINGS*...!

THE FAMILIES DON'T WANT *PUBLICITY*, THEY'RE JUST GLAD TO HAVE THEIR SONS *BACK*. AND YOU'VE ALREADY SIGNED THE *OFFICIAL SECRETS ACT*, SO I'M SURE WE CAN TRUST *YOU* TO BE DISCREET.

HOW'S *WOLF*?

STILL IN *HOSPITAL*, BUT THE DOCTORS SAY HE'LL MAKE A *COMPLETE* RECOVERY IN A FEW *WEEKS*.

WE HAD *ONE* FATALITY, THE MAN YOU SAW SHOT BY DR GRIEF. WOLF AND ANOTHER MAN WERE *INJURED*. OTHERWISE, IT WAS A *COMPLETE SUCCESS*.

YOU **LEFT** ME THERE. I CALLED FOR HELP AND YOU **DIDN'T COME.** GRIEF WAS GOING TO **KILL** ME, BUT **YOU DIDN'T CARE.**

I USED TO THINK BEING A SPY WOULD BE **EXCITING** AND **SPECIAL.** BUT YOU JUST **USED** ME. IN A WAY, YOU'RE AS BAD AS **GRIEF.** YOU'LL DO **ANYTHING** TO GET WHAT YOU WANT.

IT DOESN'T MATTER. I'VE HAD **ENOUGH.** I DON'T WANT TO BE A **SPY** ANY MORE. IF YOU ASK ME AGAIN, I'LL **REFUSE.**

I KNOW YOU THINK YOU CAN **BLACKMAIL** ME, BUT THAT WON'T WORK ANY MORE. I **KNOW** TOO MUCH.

THAT'S NOT **TRUE!** THERE WERE **DIFFICULTIES...**

WELL, **I** WANT TO GO BACK TO SCHOOL. NEXT TIME, YOU CAN DO IT **WITHOUT** ME.

HE'LL BE BACK.

YOU REALLY **THINK** SO?

HE'S TOO **GOOD** AT THE JOB. IT'S IN HIS **BLOOD.**

MOST SCHOOLBOYS **DREAM** OF BEING A SPY. ALEX IS A SPY WHO DREAMS OF BEING A **SCHOOLBOY.**

JACK? I'M BACK ... WHAT'S FOR LUNCH?

OH, ALEX! I THOUGHT YOU'D ONLY JUST GONE *OUT* AGAIN.

THE *SCHOOL* CALLED A FEW MINUTES AGO. SOMEONE CALLED *MR BRAY* WANTS TO SEE YOU AT THREE O'CLOCK.

BRAY'S THE *HEADMASTER.*

HE PROBABLY WANTS TO SEE ME ABOUT MY *ABSENCES* AGAIN.

NO, I'LL HAVE SOMETHING WHEN I GET *BACK.* SEE YOU LATER!

IT'S *TWENTY TO THREE* NOW. I'D BETTER GET *GOING.*

WHAT ABOUT YOUR *LUNCH?* SHALL I MAKE YOU A SANDWICH?

BROOKLAND SCHOOL

YOU AGAIN!

HELLO, BERNIE.

ON YOUR WAY TO SEE *MR BRAY?*

YEAH.

HE NEVER TOLD *ME* HE WAS GOING TO BE HERE TODAY.

BUT THEN, HE NEVER TELLS ME *ANYTHING!*

I'LL BE BACK AT *FIVE* TO LOCK UP. MAKE SURE YOU'RE OUT BY THEN.

OK. SEE YOU, BERNIE!

SCIENCE
BLOCK

KNOCK
KNOCK

COME IN!

YOU WANTED
TO *SEE* ME?

I'VE BEEN LOOKING **FORWARD** TO THIS.

WHAT ARE YOU **DOING** HERE? IT'S ALL OVER. THE **GEMINI PROJECT** IS **FINISHED**. YOU MIGHT AS WELL TURN YOURSELF **IN**, YOU NEED **HELP**.

THERE'S ONLY **ONE** THING **I** NEED, AND THAT'S TO SEE YOU **DEAD**.

YOU KILLED MY **FATHER!**

YOUR FATHER WAS A **TEST-TUBE!** YOU'RE A **FREAK**, HANDMADE IN THE ALPS LIKE A **CUCKOO CLOCK!**

WHAT ARE YOU GOING TO DO, TAKE MY **PLACE?** YOU WOULDN'T LAST A **WEEK**. YOU'VE GOT **"FAKE"** WRITTEN ALL **OVER** YOU!

WE COULD HAVE HAD **EVERYTHING!** WE COULD HAVE HAD THE **WHOLE WORLD!**

I DON'T **CARE** WHAT HAPPENS TO ME NOW ... AS LONG AS YOU'RE **DEAD!**

UNH...

BLAM

WHERE ARE YOU *GOING*, ALEX?

HA HA HA!

WHACK!

THE END

ANTHONY HOROWITZ (BA/Nielsen Author of the Year) is one of the most popular children's writers working today. His hugely successful Alex Rider series has sold over ten million copies worldwide and won numerous awards, including the Children's Book of the Year Award for ARK ANGEL at the British Book Awards and the Red House Children's Book Award for SKELETON KEY. He scripted the blockbuster movie STORMBREAKER from his own novel, and also writes extensively for TV, with programmes including MIDSOMER MURDERS, COLLISION, INJUSTICE and FOYLE'S WAR. Anthony Horowitz is the author of THE HOUSE OF SILK: THE NEW SHERLOCK HOLMES NOVEL. He is married to television producer Jill Green and lives in Clerkenwell with his two sons, Nicholas and Cassian, and the ghost of their dog, Lucky.

www.anthonyhorowitz.com

ANTONY JOHNSTON, who wrote the script for this book, is a veteran author of comics and graphic novels, from superheroes such as DAREDEVIL and WOLVERINE, to science-fiction adventures like WASTELAND and DEAD SPACE, and even thrillers such as THE COLDEST CITY and JULIUS. He also writes videogames, including many of the DEAD SPACE series, and other games like BINARY DOMAIN and XCOM. His debut fiction novel FRIGHTENING CURVES won an IPPY award for Best Horror. Antony lives in North-West England with his partner Marcia, his dogs Connor and Rosie, and far too many gadgets with apples printed on them.

www.antonyjohnston.com

The artwork in this graphic novel is the work of two artists, **KANAKO DAMERUM** and **YUZURU TAKASAKI,** who collaborate on every illustration. Although living on opposite sides of the globe, these Japanese sisters work seamlessly together via the Internet.

Living and working in Tokyo, **YUZURU** produced all the line work for these illustrations using traditional means. The quality of her draughtsmanship comes from years of honing her skills in the highly competitive world of manga.

KANAKO lives and works out of her studio in London. She managed and directed the project as well as colouring and rendering the artwork digitally using her wealth of knowledge in graphic design.

www.manga-media.com
www.thorogood.net

Collect all the Alex Rider books

ALEX RIDER MISSION 1 : *STORMBREAKER*
ANTHONY HOROWITZ

ALEX RIDER MISSION 2 : *POINT BLANC*
ANTHONY HOROWITZ

ALEX RIDER MISSION 3 : *SKELETON KEY*
ANTHONY HOROWITZ

ALEX RIDER MISSION 4 : *EAGLE STRIKE*
ANTHONY HOROWITZ

ALEX RIDER MISSION 5 : *SCORPIA*
ANTHONY HOROWITZ

ALEX RIDER MISSION 6 : *ARK ANGEL*
ANTHONY HOROWITZ

ALEX RIDER MISSION 7 : *SNAKEHEAD*
ANTHONY HOROWITZ

ALEX RIDER MISSION 8 : *CROCODILE TEARS*
ANTHONY HOROWITZ

ALEX RIDER MISSION 9 : *SCORPIA RISING*
ANTHONY HOROWITZ

and the graphic novels

ALEX RIDER
ANTHONY HOROWITZ
ANTONY JOHNSTON
KANAKO AND YUZURU
THE GRAPHIC NOVEL
STORMBREAKER

ALEX RIDER
ANTHONY HOROWITZ
ANTONY JOHNSTON
KANAKO AND YUZURU
THE GRAPHIC NOVEL
SKELETON KEY

ALEX RIDER
ANTHONY HOROWITZ
ANTONY JOHNSTON
KANAKO AND YUZURU
THE GRAPHIC NOVEL
EAGLE STRIKE

alexrider.com